Wilf and Wilma were at the pond.

The net got stuck.

"Help me pull," said Wilf.

They pulled the net.

It was stuck on some junk.

Wilma got a big stick.

"Let's pull it out," she said.

Wilf and Wilma pulled.

They couldn't pull the junk out.

Mum and Dad helped.

They pulled out an old pram.

Plop! A frog hopped out.

It made Wilf jump.

Splash! A fish jumped up.

“A pram full of fish,” said Dad.

“Pram dipping!” said Wilma.